LIVE IT UP,
ANDY CAPP!

Smythe

A FAWCETT GOLD MEDAL BOOK

Fawcett Publications, Inc., Greenwich, Connecticut

LIVE IT UP, ANDY CAPP!

ANDY CAPP of the Daily Mirror, London

Printed in the United States of America
May 1974

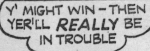

YER COULD ASK ME WHAT SORT OF A GAME I'VE 'AD, OUT OF COMMON POLITENESS!

I WOULDN'T BE SO NAIVE, SWEET'EART — I KNOW YOU ALWAYS 'AVE A BRILLIANT GAME!

IT'S TRUE. EITHER THE GAME 'E WAS GOIN'.T' PLAY, THE GAME 'E DID PLAY, OR THE GAME 'E THOUGHT 'E PLAYED

BAR

HEY, DID YOU TAKE SOME MONEY OUT OF THE TILL WHILE MY BACK WAS TURNED LAS'NIGHT?

TO BE HONEST, I DID — I TOOK ME BUS FARE 'OME

AN' WHEN DID YOU MOVE T' THE OUTER HEBRIDES?!

Smythe

3-18-72   Smythe

EMPLOYMENT
EXCHANGE

WE 'AVEN'T SEEN YOU LATELY — IS IT ANYTHIN' WE'VE SAID?!

WHY WASTE YOUR TIME AN' MINE? AUTOMATION'S TAKEN OVER

NOT YET, MATE — THEY 'AVEN'T INVENTED A MACHINE THAT DOES ABSOLUTELY NOTHIN' !!

I'LL GET 'IM ON ME WAY BACK

'ELLO, FLO! WHAT D'YER FEEL LIKE?

3-28-72

I FEEL LIKE A SIDE DISH 'E 'ADN'T ORDERED, PERCY—

ER— SORRY, I'LL 'AVE A SMALL PORT

5-19-72   Smythe

PLAY THE GAME, YOU SELFISH LITTLE DEVIL...

I'VE 'AD MY FUN, PET, SO COME AN' 'AVE YOURS!

5-30-72

BONK!

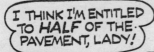
I THINK I'M ENTITLED TO *HALF* OF THE PAVEMENT, LADY!

SURE YOU ARE - AN' AS SOON AS I FIND OUT WHICH HALF I'LL BE DELIGHTED TO LET YOU 'AVE IT!

TEMPER, TEMPER

Smythe

FAWCETT GOLD MEDAL BOOKS
in the ANDY CAPP series
by Smythe

ANDY CAPP, MAN OF THE HOUR	R2762	60¢
ANDY CAPP SOUNDS OFF	R2760	60¢
ANDY CAPP STRIKES BACK (*Abridged*)	R2358	60¢
ANDY CAPP, THE ONE AND ONLY	R2436	60¢
HATS OFF TO ANDY CAPP	R2478	60¢
HURRAY FOR ANDY CAPP (*Abridged*)	R2756	60¢
IN YOUR EYE, ANDY CAPP (*Abridged*)	R2410	60¢
IT'S PUB TIME, ANDY CAPP	R2740	60¢
LIVE IT UP, ANDY CAPP	T2965	75¢
MEET ANDY CAPP	R2675	60¢
TAKE A BOW, ANDY CAPP	R2417	60¢
THE UNDISPUTED ANDY CAPP	R2649	60¢
VERY SNEAKY, ANDY CAPP	R2273	60¢
WATCH YOUR STEP, ANDY CAPP	R2899	60¢
WHAT NEXT, ANDY CAPP	R2661	60¢
YOU'RE A RIOT, ANDY CAPP	R2761	60¢
YOU'RE SOME HERO, ANDY CAPP	R2441	60¢
YOU'RE THE BOSS, ANDY CAPP	R2583	60¢
YOU TELL 'EM, ANDY CAPP	R2369	60¢

Wherever Paperbacks Are Sold

If your bookdealer is sold out, send cover price plus 15¢ each for postage and handling to Mail Order Department, Fawcett Publications, Inc., Greenwich, Connecticut 06830. Please order by number and title. Catalog available on request.